D1453654

Praise for *The Hospice Doctor's Widow*

"A beautiful tribute to caregivers and survivors."
— Rachel Reichblum, founder of That Good Grief

"I am spellbound by this wonderful book. I finished it in one evening because I couldn't stop turning pages to see what special thoughts and collaged items were next. It made me cry . . . but that's okay."
— Diana B. Denholm, PhD, author of *The Caregiving Wife's Handbook*

"Altogether different from the many books which address grief and loss from psychological or philosophical points of view, *The Hospice Doctor's Widow* is a collage of experiences, documents, tips, and those thoughts many have but few acknowledge. O'Brien's singularly moving and beautiful book maps one woman's journey, illuminating the road that lies ahead for all of us."
— Nina Corwin, LCSW, Author of *The Uncertainty of Maps*

"Eloquent and intimate. Informative without the trappings of self-help."
— Marney Rich Keenan, retired career columnist for *The Detroit News*

"This raw and beautiful book describes loving someone that you know you will lose. Just as life is full of pain and joy, so is caregiving and navigating this 'other world' of life with a serious illness. *The Hospice Doctor's Widow* encourages early and honest conversations and can help with meaningful time together as well as preparations."
— Sarah Beth Harrington, MD. Program Director – Palliative Care, University of Arkansas for Medical Sciences

"This resource fills a gap between what I provide for my patients and what their family caregivers need. I have kept my advance copy and loaned it to each of the caregivers for the three patients I recently diagnosed with ALS." — Robert Silzer, MD, Neurologist

"A very moving and lovely work, this is so different from other books I have read that chronicle the time spent with a loved one in preparation for dying. It is wise while pragmatic, beautiful and accessible, loving and personal without venturing into the trivial." — Stephen "Steppe" Mette, MD, Senior Vice Chancellor for UAMS Health and Chief Executive Officer for UAMS Medical Center at the University of Arkansas for Medical Sciences

"I smiled. I teared. I loved it. A heartwarming love story and practical guide in one. Everyone facing death, their own or a loved one's, could profit from the wisdom shared here." — Jon Mourot, PhD, Counseling Psychologist

"There are no words to convey both the practical and emotive power of this book. An incredibly difficult, dark subject filtered through a unique prism, this is something not only helpful but very, very beautiful." — Josh Gottlieb, Yogi

the
HOSPICE
DOCTOR'S
WIDOW
a journal

JENNIFER A. O'BRIEN

etaliapress.com
Little Rock, Arkansas
2020

A portion of the proceeds will be donated to the Robert W. Lehmberg, MD, Educational Fund for Palliative Care University of Arkansas for Medical Sciences (UAMS) at Winthrop P. Rockefeller Cancer Institute (WPRCI) Foundation.

Text and layout design by Jennifer A. O'Brien, except as otherwise noted
Cover design by Amy Ashford, ashford-design-studio.com

ISBN: 978-1-944528-09-6
Library of Congress Control Number: 2019054592
Cataloging in Publication Data applied for and available on request

Et Alia Press titles are available at special discounts when purchased in quantity directly from the Press. For details, contact etaliapressbooks@gmail.com or the address below.

Published in the United States of America by:
Et Alia Press
PO Box 7948
Little Rock, AR 72217
etaliapressbooks@gmail.com
etaliapress.com

for the survivors
forever changed, still here

Bob,

Have no doubt about yourself
but especially have no doubt
about my everlasting,
evergrowing love for you.
I am here.
I am in.
My heart is pure.
My love is true.

evermore yours,

jen

Precious Time

He has helped families understand
by telling them they were into
"Precious Time."
Meaning death is likely, if not imminent.

Precious Time is when you say
what you need to say and don't say
what you will later regret.

Now, it is us. We are into Precious Time.
He's going to die of this disease and
I will go on and have to live with
how I handled our Precious Time.

EAT LOTS A FISH

He helps
patients understand the personalization of end-of-life
choices by telling them about his own parents.
"My dad wanted only to be kept comfortable.
My mother wanted every last,
life-extending measure.
We honored both
of their wishes
because
the right
choice for
a person
is their
own."

Desiderata by Max Ehrmann

He keeps a sheet of paper
with this poem on it in a
drawer in our bathroom.

We read it to each other most
mornings when we are getting
ready for work.

Sometimes we read it in a
silly voice, sometimes in a
serious one.

Either way, it's a meaningful
moment together.
Centers us for the day we
each have ahead.

e-mail update

Yesterday we had a visit with the oncologist. We learned that the origin of the malignant, metastatic tumor is renal. This is much better news than what we were told on Tuesday night, which was that the origin was unknown and could be melanoma.

Brain MRI this morning was clear, which was expected.

Tomorrow morning is the PET scan which is another big rule-out opportunity. If no big operative masses show up on that, then no surgery.

The pathology is being sent to a lab in Houston, where they will analyze it for a possible medication match (sometimes they select the medication based on the genetic make up of the tumor(s)). This will take a couple of weeks.

We still have a very long, potentially rough road ahead but this news is very good.

Some renal cancers can be cured with medication.

You are welcome to share this information with anyone.

love,
jen

Tomorrow will be the first garbage day since learning my husband is dying of cancer.

The sun is not out again today.
It's a big problem.

As a physician working at a world-renowned, treatment center, he cares for patients and families from all over the world. Sometimes patients are too sick to make the trip home and have to die in our town.

That always breaks his heart He is glad to be part of a center of excellence, but several times a year he comes home from work saddened. "I just can't get this patient home to die," he says.

He understands the desire to travel for the best care, but he is always troubled when people push it a little too long or have a complication and have to be away from their community when they die.

HOPE FOR THE BEST & PREPARE FOR THE WORST

The "best" and the "worst" change over time ....
At first, the best may be a cure and the worst is death.
Then, the best may become laughter and appreciation
and the worst is pain and suffering ....

When people say, "You are in my prayers," it makes me cry.
I appreciate the sentiment
but I don't want to NEED
to be in anyone's prayers.

I liked it when he was the healthy physician
and other families were in OUR prayers.
Why can't it be like that again?
I think to myself, as I smile
a grateful, quiet smile
and swallow the lump
in my throat.

This is us. My husband, who hates having his picture taken, said after receiving the diagnosis, "If you want a good picture of me, we need to take it soon." Luckily, I mentioned it to a photographer I met, who followed up with me a few days later.

I am so grateful for that follow up because I am not sure I would have taken the initiative. I was in a state of denial . . . I had thought about having our picture taken but was saddened by the reason for it. On some level, I thought I could postpone the inevitable by delaying the picture.

The picture perfectly captures our love and happiness.

Someday soon, I will cherish this photo even more because looking at it will help me recreate the feeling of his arms around me.

Anticipatory Grief: grieving before your loved one actually dies. It's real. It can be HUGE. In one study, 40% of widows reported Anticipatory Grief as worse than the grief after the death.

I am suffering from Anticipatory Grief.

The key is honoring my Anticipatory Grief while not allowing it to spoil the time we have left together.

13

He wants to be cremated. He wants me to scatter his ashes over my brother's grave as I did with my mother's ashes. Bob and I had a beautiful visit to David's grave a couple of years ago. Going back to scatter his ashes will be difficult, but knowing that I am doing exactly what he wants will be comforting.

I love that we have had the courage to discuss what he wants. My mother and I had that, and it made all the difference for me as the survivor.

Excerpt from Gathering Hope Life Review
Clark Smith, MD, interviewing patient, Robert Lehmberg, MD

So now that I have stage IV disease, I've had a new experience — the experience of being faced with the end of life. It was more frightening than I thought it would be. I got the biopsy and the ENT guy called me and said, "Well, this is some kind of clear cell/undifferentiated/whatever . . ." It still didn't quite sink in. I said, "What? I don't know what you are talking about." I got a PET scan early the next morning and went in and looked at it. The radiologist said, "Y' know, Bob, we've been friends for a long time, this is not good news. I gotta tell you. It's in your thoracic spine, and it's in your supraclavicular nodes, and it's in your retroperitoneal nodes. This is not a good deal."

I thought, well, gosh, well, we'll work it out. And I tried to go to work later that morning. I couldn't stop crying. I'm terrified. I am so scared I can't stand it! As usual, I wasn't quite as tough as I thought I was. The first two or three days, it was frightening. I came home to Jennifer a few times and just cried. I couldn't imagine not being here. I couldn't imagine. What, how is this gonna work? I've always been here; how can I not be here?

But actually, after that went away, I went to see the oncologist. I said to him, 'This is palliative right?" He said, "We're not going to talk about that." I had the genetic testing. Apparently, if you're fortunate and you've got a genetic malformation, those can sometimes be cured with targeted therapy, but this wasn't. I said, "Well, if you think it's worth it, start me on something and we'll see how it goes."

It's been okay; it's not terrible. Tired. But it's not awful.

Pretty much always feel better
once the bed is made
and the bedroom is straightened.
Some days,
I feel A LOT better.

Oh,
and
coffee
helps.

There's a woman he texts with periodically. She is a cancer survivor. She survived her cancer but apparently her marriage did not. Happens more than you think, he "explains." I think to myself, Oh, I am certain it does.

If I am honest, there are times when I want to just go. But I play it out and realize leaving would mean living without what we have and with myself after having run from my greatest love and duty.

Still, this texting gets under my skin. There is an exclusive, you-wouldn't-understand air he seems to put on when he does it. Of course, I don't understand.

Post Mortem Note: I never learned who his cancer buddy was. I am grateful to her. He needed her. We both did.

17

We're going through different processes

2

He
is
dying

I
am
surviving

Even the most basic tasks require the utmost concentration so that I don't end up complicating our situation further by having a wreck or slicing my hand while making a salad.

Our best friends
in this
are those who
check in frequently, yet
have no expectations
of a response.

(Preferrably by text message.)

e-mail update

Let me begin by saying Bob and I feel very lucky in many ways. Lucky that we found this cancer while he is still physically able to do what means most to him.

After the radiation on the spine metastises, June was SO good for us. We went on the vacation of a lifetime in Montreal, where every day we enjoyed a city neither of us had experienced and had lots of wonderful time together.

We came home and prepared for our 5th (and final) annual UAMS/VA Palliative Care Program party. We had a great turnout of all the physicians, nurses, social workers, chaplains, and their families. The food was delicious and everyone seemed to have a good time. We had a dear friend stay with us for a week. We feel extremely fortunate.

Bob is working at the VA hospital and still has a faculty role at UAMS. We have realized as we've settled into this reality that his work is of the utmost importance to him in feeling fulfilled in his remaining time. Bob underwent two courses of an oral chemo. The treatment was easy on Bob; he experienced NO side effects. He has felt good. Working out, enjoying good and healthy food.

Yesterday, he underwent the PET scan to follow up and compare to the March PET scan to see if the chemo had worked at slowing the growth of the cancer. It had not. The number and size of the retroperitoneal tumors have increased. This was disappointing news. On the bright side, there is no additional metastatic bone disease. This is really good. Metastatic bone disease is painful and makes the bones brittle and fragile.

continuation of e-mail

So, his oncologist has taken him off that chemo and has another oral chemotherapy that he is going to start him on. Bob will take that for 2-3 months when we will do another PET scan to see if it has slowed the growth of the cancer.

That's the best we can hope for, to slow the growth of the cancer. None of these chemotherapies will cure the cancer; we know that. We are just hoping to get additional time. With each new medication we weigh whether the potential side effects will be worth the additional time we may or may not get.

Bob and I are both disappointed that the cancer has progressed. I think we really felt/hoped that chemo was working to slow the growth, however, I cannot stress enough how fortunate we both feel. We are so lucky that we met each other. We have proof positive that our love is big and true. Bob, from his profession, and I, from personal experience, know what *Precious Time* is and we are enjoying it.

We have been able to have conversations about what he wants and doesn't want in end-of-life care and I am confident that I can honor all of his wishes. Better still, we have some time. We started to talk last night about our next trip. :-)

As always, I hope you will forward this email. It's really difficult to write these emails so I appreciate your willingness to forward.

Thanks for keeping us in your thoughts and prayers.

with love and faith,

jennifer

If I don't get out of this house soon, he is not going to live to die of cancer and I will do life without parole.

Tonight we were cuddled up, enjoying watching television together and an ad for a chemotherapy came on and ruined the rare carefree moment.

Are there any true stories about patients who were actually helped by those advertisements?

Helped by the chemo itself? Yes. But is anyone helped by the direct-to-consumer ads for chemotherapies?

If you do not believe that kindness,
patience, and love are life-sustaining,
just ask Bob.
He will tell you he is living proof.

It has been months
since we got his diagnosis.
While the healthcare he has received
is unmatched in quality,
he has said many times
it is the love and kindness
that have kept him alive.

e-mail update

Sent: December 8
To: Family and Friends
Subject: Update - 9 Months from Diagnosis

Hope for the best and prepare for the worst is a mission that is simple but by no means easy.

Bob had a PET scan last week and there was very little tumor growth. While we still have hopes that this second chemotherapy might actually shrink/eliminate the cancer, right now we consider very little tumor growth success. Bob's oncologist told him he could shop for summer clothes, so there is that! :-)

We are not able to travel by air during cold and flu season because Bob is especially susceptible, but we did drive up to St. Louis for Thanksgiving where Bob's niece is in her intern year of Pediatrics. The rest of Bob's family met us and we had a lovely visit. Travel takes a lot out of him these days, so we're going to spend the rest of the holiday season in Little Rock.

We have done, and continue, a purge, which has been a gift to me because if I had been left to do it by myself it would have been overwhelming and heartbreaking. There has been a lot of interest in our house and we are very serious about selling it, so that we can move into something smaller with less upkeep and enjoy more time just being together.
Thanks for thinking of us.
xo,
jen

Conclusion from Gathering Hope Life Review
Clark Smith, MD, interviewing patient, Robert Lehmberg, MD

Things are finally good. And I think this is going to go well for me. I wish I could make it go well for Jennifer, but you can't do anything about that. I can try to help her, but I can't make it happen. I don't know how that's gonna go for her. She's pretty fragile at times. That's probably the only worry I have in my life right now. I'm a lot more worried about that than I am dying, honestly. I mean, I truly believe that dying is a peaceful process. I've seen it enough. No matter what happens after you die, no matter what you believe, the actual *dying* is peaceful.

Interviewer Clark Smith, MD: It's like you always said, the patients are gonna be okay, it's the family . . .

Yes, the patient's gonna be fine. It's the family. Well, that's true. The patient is gonna be fine. And so far leading up to this, I've been okay, except for one terrified day or two. I've seen enough death now to know it's just that—the patient's gonna be fine. I have absolutely no idea what comes next. I don't know. I hope I've met all the requirements. Who knows? Hope I didn't do anything too bad.

* * *

I am taking the time to make
the most of tender touch
and smell moments.
I will be able to look at pictures.
I'll hear his voice in my head.
But feeling his skin and deeply
inhaling his smell will
elude me forever.
I will miss that so.

What's on your mind?

Sometimes it gives me great refuge
to check social media —
lightens things,
makes me smile
and feel connected.

Other times, I get there
and find everyone else is carefree.
Never know which it will be
until it's the latter and it's too late.

(I want to be worried about where to find
almond oil for a mai tai recipe.)

The book cover:

How wife and husband can communicate and relate better — and make good choices during his illness so that their life together meets the needs of both.

The
CAREGIVING WIFE'S HANDBOOK

Caring for Your Seriously Ill Husband,
Caring for Yourself

" Denholm provides psychological insights and practical advice about how to keep mind and body healthy while negotiating some of the most difficult challenges one can face in a marriage. If you are supporting a husband who is terminally ill, this is a must-read. "

— DAVID L. SHERN, PhD, PRESIDENT AND CEO, MENTAL HEALTH AMERICA

DIANA B. DENHOLM, PhD, LMHC

This book is extremely helpful, not just in its content but because every time he notices me reading it, he seems to be reminded that what we are going through isn't just all about him.

Also, it has provided some great discussion for us. She describes typical challenges—men who won't wear the diaper despite the obvious need. I asked him about it. He said, "Oh, I see it all the time. Not sure what it is but lots of guys refuse to wear the diaper." He added, "You do not have to worry about that with me. If the time comes, I will be man enough to wear the diaper."

Post Mortem Note:
If I ever get serious with a man again, a good screening question might be — Are you man enough to wear the diaper?

Imperceptible to others, I see it. Feel it.
Each night his muscle mass
is less and less.

He likes when I rub on his head as we lie in bed;
it makes him feel loved.

I think about how much I will miss the feel of his skin
and hair under my finger tips. Sometimes it makes
me too sad, so I read while I do it.
I want him to feel loved.

I won't allow my
sadness to usurp the
touch time we have left.

We had the foresight to transfer the cars and other property
to my name. When the notary public made a comment
about why we were doing it, we told her Bob was dying.
She squirmed uncomfortably. I said, "We're at peace with it,"
something I had heard Bob say to others.

For the most part it is true.
At end of life, people die; I wish more people would accept that openly.
We're not at war with it; we're at peace with the fact that
at the end of life comes death. We are facing the tasks
of getting things in order so that when the time comes, I will only have
to love him, mourn his death, and miss him.

The televison in the waiting or infusion room of a healthcare facilty never provides comfort or reassurance. Absolutely none. Ever.

e-mail update

Sent: September 16

To: Family and Friends

Subject: 18 Months from Diagnosis

A CT last week showed that Bob's disease continues to grow slowly.
He has many lesions in his retroperitoneum, one in each hip, a small one in
his thoracic spine, on both sides of his neck, etc. He has lost about 50 lbs
since the onset of the disease. At this point we have tried four different
chemotherapies. We don't really know if a couple of the chemotherapies
helped to slow the disease progression. We do know, however, that with a
couple of them Bob has experienced side effects of the sort that make one
wonder if the treatment is worse than the disease.

Bob made it through the end of the academic year (June 30) working his
regular schedule but had to stop in July because of pain, fatigue, and side
effects of the treatments. He's still doing some work for a committee of the
Arkansas State Medical Board and hopes to be able to go to Journal Club
and resume participation in some other work in the UAMS & VA Palliative
Care Program. As this most recent side effect (excruciating pain in the
soles of his feet) subsides, Bob and his oncologist will decide if he is going
to try a fifth chemotherapy. Side effects, co-morbidities, risks, and the cold
and flu season ahead have led us to have essential discussions about
Bob's preferences and wishes.

We used to have good trips, good weeks; now we have good days, good
moments—and they are really good. :-) We have hopes of visiting Bob's
family in Texas during the holidays, so we will see if he is up to the trips.
We still consider ourselves lucky in so many ways, however, we have
definitely begun to transition from Hope to Peace. And while Hope and
Peace both sound like great places to be, the passage between
is extraordinarily difficult.

The miracle is peace.

with love,

jen o.

Yesterday, we cried together about how much we will miss each other when he dies.

We are becoming closer and closer and it feels so good. I must have faith. What other choice do I have?

I can't pull away. . . The regret after he dies will be unbearable. I want to KNOW that I loved him thoroughly. That's my goal from now until he is gone.

And when he is gone,
I'll be alone.

Sometimes I wish I would be diagnosed with cancer and beat him to the finish line.

This morning I found this note taped inside his bathroom cabinet.

in acceptance lies peace

BEAT
WARRIOR
battle
FIGHT
CONQUER

I am so weary of the war language used in describing disease. His sister texts, "We'll conquer this." Obituaries report, "_____ lost his battle with cancer."

This is so much more than winning or losing.

Disease is a journey that calls for strength, sadness, believing, planning, hope, endurance, patience, joy, flexibility, mindfulness, resilience, and a sense of humor.

Time and energy spent fighting the disease is not spent on loving each other and being together. This is a process and at the end, he dies— not because he is a loser or weak, but because at the end of life comes death.

When he dies we'll say, "He lived a full life." We'll say, "He served his community as a physician." We'll say, "He was loved and will be missed." We WON'T say he lost.

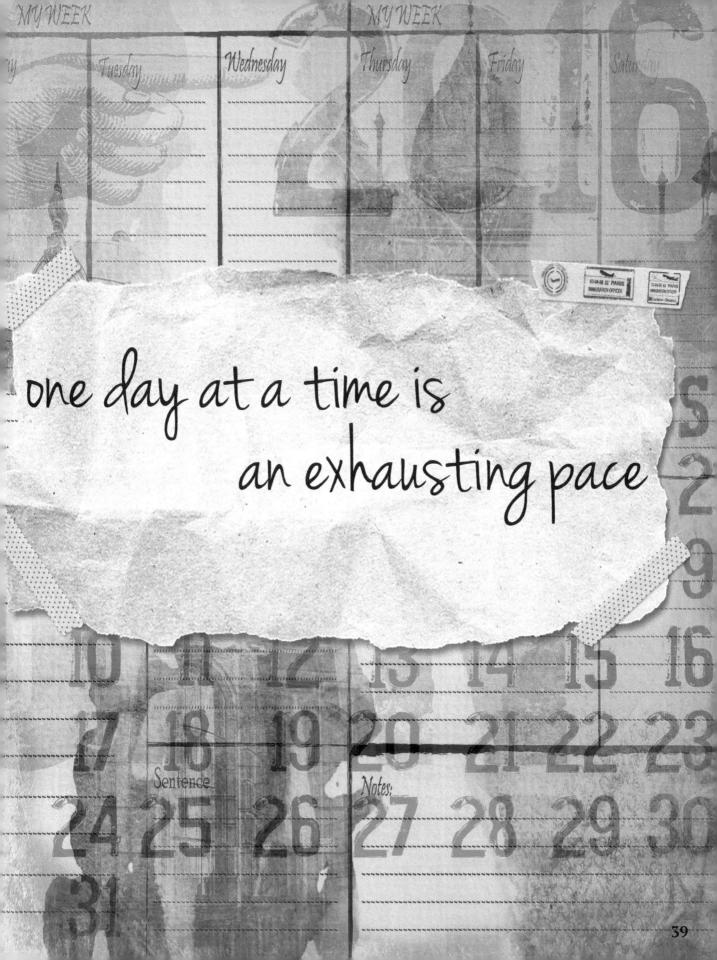

one day at a time is
an exhausting pace

He eats only ice cream and yogurt.
Real food hurts his mouth.
I know this is common for people getting chemotherapy.
Thankfully, I am no cook.
At first, I thought it would be fun
for us to have a good reason
to eat all the ice cream both of us wanted.

Even ice cream is sad now.

Excerpt from Gathering Hope Life Review
Clark Smith, MD, interviewing patient, Robert Lehmberg, MD

Question: What are your thoughts on Palliative Care?

Answer: It's about not hurrying death,
        not extending life,
        not being attached to the outcome.

Being willing to "meet the patient where they are." Every single day, I walk out of that hospital and say, "That was an amazing day. That was an amazing experience." I not only can tolerate it, but I like it. I like the intensity. I'm aware of that. That may or may not be a good reason to do it. One of the first things people would ask me is, "What's Palliative Care? What do you do?" Well, the trick is walking into somebody's room that you have never met before in your whole life, and having to establish a trusting relationship in about 15 minutes. Y'know? That's tricky, and I've screwed it up plenty of times. You gotta think about it, your loved one's dying, this guy walks in and says, "I need to talk to you about how this is gonna go, what we're gonna do, what you want, what you don't want, what's realistic, what's not."

You've got to be able to focus on the person, give them your full attention, communicate clearly. I mean, it's tricky. Everyone thinks they can do it, but they can't, they really can't.

It's hard work.

It's self awareness.

Palliative Care is a team approach that may include:

Goals of Care

Specialized Social Work

Chaplaincy

Hospice Transition

Symptom Management

Pain Management

Guidance for Caregivers

Advanced Practice Nursing

Additional Professional Help

Bereavement Counseling

depending on the needs & wishes of the patient & loved ones

A Palliative Care team includes a physician, advanced practice nurse, social worker, and chaplain. Bob loved being part of a team. Ideally, Palliative Care is brought in early. They help the patient and family learn the new reality of living with the condition. Palliative Care helps with the symptoms, pain, side effects, and the psycho-social aspects that go along with the condition & the treatments. Bob had Palliative Care patients whose care lasted for years and some who didn't need him anymore because of remission or cure. Palliative Care does not mean the patient is dying. It is not the same as Hospice. IF/when there are no treatments left, or the patient does not want additional treatments, the Palliative Care team can help transition to Hospice.

The Hospice Team offers the same range of support and resources when end of life is the focus.

That's how it's supposed to work.
We didn't have that.
Ours was DIY Palliative Care.
I don't recommend it.

CAUTION

we are our worst
selves in fear

we are our best
selves in vulnerability

We have the miracle
of acceptance.

(or do we?)

I will not miss the sleepless nights filled with his relentless moaning, wheezing, and suffering.

I will not miss trying, yet failing, to comfort him.

I will not miss wrapping his swollen legs. I will not miss giving him injections.

I will not miss changing the sheets in the middle of the night because of his night sweats.

I will miss loving someone so much that I do all of those things.

Tonight he asked if I am
having an affair!

I am hurt and angry but
mostly I know he loves me and
he is just feeling out of control.

(When does he think
I have time to see this lover?)

We get into patterns
of griping at each other.

I think he might feel better if he eats.
He doesn't want to eat.
He snaps at me.
I snap back at him.
We both feel hurt and alone.

It's up to me to shatter the patterns.
The first step
is admitting you have a pattern.

He said to his cousin,
"I am planning my memorial service."
She interrupted,
"Oh, you're not going to need one of those!"

He died three weeks later.
(Aren't we all going to need one of those?)

Another chemo had to be stopped because of life-threatening side effects. The oncologist has offered yet another drug option and Bob is faced again with deciding if he wants to try this one. He'll read and understand all of the literature on the new chemotherapy, knowing that many of the possible side effects or complications could make an already difficult disease process far worse. He knows that some side effects could mean an awful death. Like many physicians, he has definite thoughts on how he does not want to die.

All I know to do is support him in the decision he makes. It's his decision, not mine.

He never did take that last chemotherapy.
He lived for three more months.
He died from the cancer,
rather than some awful side effect of a drug.
He died the way he wanted to.

Treatment Decisions

- Understand the proposed treatment objective:

  Palliative - to relieve pain and provide comfort,
      to enhance quality of life with the disease
    but not to cure the disease.

  Cure - to heal, make well.

  Slow disease progression - to provide more time
    but not to cure the disease.

- Is there an upcoming event (wedding, birth of a child, anniversary, reunion) to try to be present for?
      Worth risking side effects?
- What are the possible, life-threatening side effects?
- Disease fatigue is simply being tired of treatments,
    illness, side effects, etc.

      Remember, a decision is not permanent.
        You can always change your mind.

He is writing good-bye letters
to some of the people he loves.
(I know he won't write one to me.)
I'm a little envious of those who will
be receiving these letters, which I am
stamping and taking to the post office.

Mostly,
I am glad he is writing the letters.

Today, I couldn't open a jar. I didn't ask him because I am certain he is too weak. My heart is broken that he is no longer my strong husband who can open jars for me. Asking him would only have broken his heart too.

He is sleeping.
The apartment is clean.
I am sitting reading the newspaper.
The similarities to caring for a newborn are remarkable.
A cycle of daily chores necessary for the absolute basics.
Thankless, endlessly repeating chores . . .
. . . making the bed, straightening, dishes, laundry.
In between, having enough presence and nurturing to give him.
Like a baby, he moans and cries, especially when the sun goes down.
It is late November! The sun is down for about 18 of the 24 hours!

He doesn't sleep well, or for very long, especially at night.
In order to fall asleep, he needs me to rub on his head
and hold him close.

I feel exhausted nearly all the time.
There are still moments of Precious Time
but it seems they are few and far between the drudgery.
Still, I know someday
I will miss the stuff that seems so exhausting now.
His phone rings. He's awake and calling for me.

e-mail update

Sent: January 11

To: Family and Friends

Subject: Home Hospice

We admitted Bob to home hospice on Monday afternoon.
He seems to be at the beginning stages of letting go.

Pray for quiet and quick. The miracle is peace.

xo,
jen

As he sleeps,
getting closer and closer to death,
I arrange this tableau to introduce
my loved ones, who have gone on before,
to my beloved who will join them very soon.

"He died peacefully with his hand in mine at 1:00 this morning,"
is what my text to family and friends read.

Death may be peaceful for the patient but it is not for the loved one
in the room. During those last hours, they don't really look like
themselves, they don't smell great, and they can be loud.
Mucus builds up in the airway and breathing is a loud rattle
— such was the case with Bob.

I knew we were at the very end. I knew he wanted me, and me alone,
with him. With each and every loud breath he took, I found myself
holding mine...waiting to see if he would take another. I finally
decided to settle in for another night in the chair beside his bed. I put
my earbuds in and turned up Mary Gauthier's, Mercy Now, an
album he had introduced me to many years prior. I could feel each word
and note just as I could feel his hand around mine.

I saw the clock strike midnight and then must have fallen asleep, which
in itself was a miracle. Next thing I knew it was 1:00am. The hospice
nurse had come in the room and said, "It's quiet in here." And sure
enough, he had died while I was asleep. My hand was still in his and
his hand was still warm. It was the last gift we gave each other.

Robert "Bob" Lehmberg, MD, died with his wife, Jennifer O'Brien, at his side, her hand in his in the early hours of January 19th.

Born to Rose Mary Lehmberg and Seth Ward Lehmberg, MD (both deceased) in Taylor, Texas, Bob got his first summer job as a hospital orderly at age 18. He knew immediately he was meant to care for patients and continued the job while earning his bachelor's from the University of Texas. During medical school, at the University of Texas Medical Branch in Galveston, Bob was immediately drawn to surgical specialties. His work, during a rotation on the plastic surgery service at the Baylor College of Medicine in Houston, earned him a residency.

He completed preceptor training under Al Blue, MD, in Seattle and a fellowship focusing on reconstructive surgery of the hand at the University of Colorado. Bob relocated to Little Rock where he practiced classic plastic and reconstructive surgery, meaning trauma, burns, congenital anomalies, hand surgery, breast reconstruction following mastectomy, and microsurgery.

He became a fellow of the American College of Surgeons and later achieved board certification in plastic and reconstructive surgery. He was appointed chief of surgery at Baptist Medical Center in Little Rock, board chairman at Columbia Doctors Hospital in Little Rock, and Assistant Professor of Plastic Surgery in the Department of Surgery at UAMS, where he taught for five years. Bob served on the hand surgery staff for the Central Arkansas Veterans Healthcare System.

In the prime of his surgical career, when a neck injury prevented him from operating, he retrained in Hospice and Palliative Medicine. He did a preceptorship with Reed Thompson, MD and completed his Palliative Medicine fellowship training under the leadership of Sarah Beth Harrington, MD at Central Arkansas Veterans Healthcare System and UAMS. He became board certified in Hospice and Palliative Medicine and joined the UAMS faculty as an Assistant Professor.

While Bob loved being a plastic surgeon, in hospice and palliative medicine, he "felt like he became the physician he was always meant to be." At UAMS and the VA, he helped train many physicians in the unique specialty and interdisciplinary team approach necessary to care for patients and families struggling with serious illness and end-of-life care.

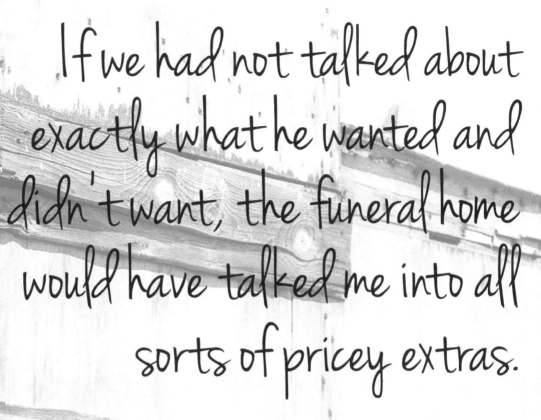

If we had not talked about exactly what he wanted and didn't want, the funeral home would have talked me into all sorts of pricey extras.

This is not a time for unnecessary expense.

He is gone.
I am undone.
All I can do is cry out to him,
Please come back.
Please, Bob, please come back.
please . . .

He made my pour-over coffee every morning.

When he became too sick to do it,

I was too busy taking care of him to do it.

After he died, one after one, relatives stayed with me.

In the morning, they would ask for coffee.

I would tearfully say, "He made the coffee."

One after one, they would teach me how to make the coffee.

I still don't make coffee for myself most mornings.

I know how.

I always knew how.

It was the love that he put into it

that made me crave the coffee.

I don't want coffee

that isn't made with his love.

Excerpt from Gathering Hope Life Review
Clark Smith, MD, interviewing patient, Robert Lehmberg, MD

Question: Are there any lessons or advice?

Answer: Aww, be nice. Be nice. So at Baylor, the surgeons were all sarcastic and fairly harsh. If you couldn't have someone in tears without raising your voice, you were a failure. You need to go back and train some more. You should be able to have somebody in tears just by being sarcastic or behaving ugly. And that's not nice, or macho. That's not something to be proud of. So, if I had it to do over again, I'd try to be nicer to people.

He was very nice. I think he had worked over the years to overcome the Baylor surgeon default he describes here... but he never completely shed it. When he was feeling particularly bad physically, he could be very ugly to me. Mean at times. I think this is true for lots of men who have terminal or chronic illness. Perhaps women too.
There's always a caregiver they are particularly tough on.
It's so difficult to be that caregiver.

Making sure he felt loved while he was being so mean was one of the greatest challenges. It took a lot of faith...
-Faith in my love for him.
-Faith in myself.
-Faith in his love for me.
KNOWING he loved me, even when he was behaving so terribly toward me.

62

Preparations we made that were very helpful to me as the survivor:

_ Advance Directives & Healthcare Power of Attorney

_ Discussion about what he wanted at end of life — palliative sedation, inpatient

_ Last Will & Testament

_ Downsized, sold, and gave away things we did not need

_ Sold our house and moved into a single-story condominium

_ Put automobiles and other property in my name

_ Saved cash for funeral and other expenses

_ Bestowed and designated belongings to specific individuals

_ Planned Memorial Service

_ Documented details for obituary

_ Completed paperwork for survivor benefits at his workplace

_ Specified handling of remains

_ Wishes for me to communicate with others (ex-wife, family) when he was no longer able to himself

Post Mortem Note:
Letting these topics come up naturally . . .

Gentle prompts . . . waiting for him to tell me. Being willing to listen and remember even when it was difficult.

Asking —
"Would you like me to . . . ?"
Rather than telling,
"We/you should . . . "

What we didn't do, but I wish we had:

_ Put utilities in my name

_ Document passwords to all technology access

63

Medication Management Lessons Learned:

Lock it up! Anything in a prescription bottle is likely to be diverted, by family, visitors, helpers, even hospice staff. Don't think YOUR friends "would never..." Once it's been taken, it's too late. Your complicated situation becomes more so when medications are diverted. (I kept his in a box so I could easily lock it up between uses.)

Set timers as reminders to give the medication. "Breakthrough pain" should not come from forgetting to take pain meds. Write it down. Keep a notebook with doses and times medications are given.

***After death, take all meds to police station or other designated safe disposal site asap.

HIM: "I'M DYING! WHAT'S THE WORST THAT CAN HAPPEN? I DIE!"

ME: "If I come upon you one night, and you have died, I know exactly what to do. But what if I walk in, and you are unconscious or seizing . . . ? You always say, 'Don't call the EMTs until I am cold.'

"What if you don't die right away? Do I sit there and wait for you to die? What if you don't? At what point is the sheriff going to look at the situation and say I was negligent? Or what if you end up in the vegetative state you have always dreaded?"

This was a heated exchange we had one morning after a particularly scary night. He was reluctant to admit himself to hospice status, not because he didn't believe in hospice; rather, I think he thought we could do it ourselves.

He wanted privacy—most people in the palliative care and hospice community here knew him.

Following this conversation he seemed to better understand my position and concerns. Soon after, he admitted himself to hospice status and died 10 days later.

Hospice status meant that if he coded, I would call hospice instead of 911. Hospice would come to help but not revive him, which was what he wanted.

everybody dies.

Sometimes,
I open his closet,
lean in and breathe deeply.
I can still smell him.

I am not suicidal
BUT
I would welcome death.

HOPE FOR THE BEST
&
PREPARE FOR THE WORST

This was the most helpful advice.
Do both. Balance them evenly.
Define "the best." Maybe it is a cure, but it is NOT forever.
No one lives forever.

For us, "the best" was Bob being able to work
and us having enjoyable, loving time together.
Still, we prepared.
Careful not to drag the other's "hope" moment
into a "prepare" moment.
Still, we prepared
and it made all the difference.

WITH LOVE

In the end,
all we really want
is to know
we have loved well
and been loved.

Recently, I read something suggesting that instead
of taking the one-day-at-a-time approach
looking forward, look back —

I made it through another day.

That has really helped me.
Each evening I congratulate myself on having
gotten through another day without him.

my gratitude

my grief

my love

FROM
HERE

A true heart.

To my Valentine

Happy New Year

MY HEART'S DEAREST.

Will you Go off with me on the

Dec. 25th

To my Valentine

73

Almost immediately, married women think you are on the prowl for their husbands now that yours is dead.

"He's mine!" one said to me at a gathering recently.

(I don't want your husband! I want mine.)

For more than
30 years I have
known AND advised
others—
the 2nd year is
harder by far.

Why am I so
surprised now?

In a way, it's better than a breakup. There is no wondering, "Why doesn't he love me anymore?"

Mistakenly,
I thought the firsts were over after a year.
First general election without him.
Cried my way through it, but I voted.

The looking back
with longing is
slowly disappearing
and I can feel
What's next?

coming on.

(I can't smell him anymore
and I make my own pour-over
coffee almost every
morning.)

I met a more recent widow than I.
She seemed especially lost.
I asked her,
"Do you talk to him?"
She was aghast,
"No, I don't think I could."
I said reassuringly,
"I understand. I talk to mine
all the time. It helps me."
She just kept repeating,
"I don't think I can . . .
I just don't think I can . . ."

"I understand," I said.

hopeace

hopeace

hopeace

hopeace

hopeace

peace

The miracle is
peace

JBien

CPSIA information can be obtained
at www.ICGtesting.com
Printed in the USA
BVHW020143180721
612006BV00002B/8